THE ROYAL HORTICULTURAL SOCIETY

DIARY 2012

Commentary by
Brent Elliott

Illustrations from
the Royal Horticultural Society's
Lindley Library

FRANCES LINCOLN LIMITED
PUBLISHERS

Frances Lincoln Limited
4 Torriano Mews
Torriano Avenue
London NW5 2RZ
www.franceslincoln.com

First Frances Lincoln edition 2011

A catalogue record for this book is available from
the British Library

ISBN: 978-0-7112-3300-3

Printed in China

1 2 3 4 5 6 7 8 9

Front cover *Camellia sasanqua* 'Crimson King',
a cultivar whose history Thomas unsuccessfully
tried to trace, and *Viburnum x bodnantense*
'Dawn'. First published in *Colour in the winter
garden* (1967).
Back cover A Multiflora Rambler rose. First
published in *Climbing roses old and new* (1965).
(Detail)
Title page *Origanum* 'Kent Beauty'. It was bred by
Elizabeth Strangman of the Washfield Nursery in
the 1970s. First published in *The complete flower
paintings* (1987). (Detail)
Overleaf, left *Rosa* 'Fru Dagmar Hastrup', a
Danish rose introduced just before the First World
War, and *Rosa* 'Roseraie de l'Hay', a Hybrid
Rugosa bred by the amateur rosarian Jules
Gravereaux in 1901. First published in *Shrub roses
of today* (1962).

**The following books by Graham Stuart Thomas
are available from Frances Lincoln:**
*Ornamental Shrubs: Climbers and Bamboos;
Perennial Garden Plants; Recollections of Great
Gardeners; The Graham Stuart Thomas Rose
Book; The Rock Garden and its Plants; Trees
in the Landscape*
www.franceslincoln.com

RHS FLOWER SHOWS 2012
Regrettably Flower Show dates are no longer
included in this diary. Show date changes after
publication caused confusion.
The following dates were correct at the time of
going to press but, due to circumstances beyond
our control, show dates often change in the
interim period so *please confirm before travelling*.
Neither the RHS or the publisher can accept
liability for any errors.
The Chelsea Flower Show (May 22–26 2012),
Hampton Court Palace Flower Show (July 3–8
2012) and **Tatton Park Flower Show** (July 18–22
2012), **Cardiff Flower Show** (April 20–22 2012),
Malvern Flower Shows (May 10–13 and Sept
29–30 2012) and themed London Shows
throughout the year.

RHS Flower Show Information
Can be found by visiting www.rhs.org.uk
or telephoning the **24-hour Flower Show
Information Line (020 7649 1885)**

CALENDAR 2012

	JANUARY		FEBRUARY		MARCH		APRIL

JANUARY
```
M  T  W  T  F  S  S
               1
2  3  4  5  6  7  8
9  10 11 12 13 14 15
16 17 18 19 20 21 22
23 24 25 26 27 28 29
30 31
```

FEBRUARY
```
M  T  W  T  F  S  S
      1  2  3  4  5
6  7  8  9  10 11 12
13 14 15 16 17 18 19
20 21 22 23 24 25 26
27 28 29
```

MARCH
```
M  T  W  T  F  S  S
         1  2  3  4
5  6  7  8  9  10 11
12 13 14 15 16 17 18
19 20 21 22 23 24 25
26 27 28 29 30 31
```

APRIL
```
M  T  W  T  F  S  S
               1
2  3  4  5  6  7  8
9  10 11 12 13 14 15
16 17 18 19 20 21 22
23 24 25 26 27 28 29
30
```

MAY
```
M  T  W  T  F  S  S
   1  2  3  4  5  6
7  8  9  10 11 12 13
14 15 16 17 18 19 20
21 22 23 24 25 26 27
28 29 30 31
```

JUNE
```
M  T  W  T  F  S  S
            1  2  3
4  5  6  7  8  9  10
11 12 13 14 15 16 17
18 19 20 21 22 23 24
25 26 27 28 29 30
```

JULY
```
M  T  W  T  F  S  S
                  1
2  3  4  5  6  7  8
9  10 11 12 13 14 15
16 17 18 19 20 21 22
23 24 25 26 27 28 29
30 31
```

AUGUST
```
M  T  W  T  F  S  S
      1  2  3  4  5
6  7  8  9  10 11 12
13 14 15 16 17 18 19
20 21 22 23 24 25 26
27 28 29 30 31
```

SEPTEMBER
```
M  T  W  T  F  S  S
               1  2
3  4  5  6  7  8  9
10 11 12 13 14 15 16
17 18 19 20 21 22 23
24 25 26 27 28 29 30
```

OCTOBER
```
M  T  W  T  F  S  S
1  2  3  4  5  6  7
8  9  10 11 12 13 14
15 16 17 18 19 20 21
22 23 24 25 26 27 28
29 30 31
```

NOVEMBER
```
M  T  W  T  F  S  S
         1  2  3  4
5  6  7  8  9  10 11
12 13 14 15 16 17 18
19 20 21 22 23 24 25
26 27 28 29 30
```

DECEMBER
```
M  T  W  T  F  S  S
               1  2
3  4  5  6  7  8  9
10 11 12 13 14 15 16
17 18 19 20 21 22 23
24 25 26 27 28 29 30
31
```

CALENDAR 2013

JANUARY
```
M  T  W  T  F  S  S
   1  2  3  4  5  6
7  8  9  10 11 12 13
14 15 16 17 18 19 20
21 22 23 24 25 26 27
28 29 30 31
```

FEBRUARY
```
M  T  W  T  F  S  S
            1  2  3
4  5  6  7  8  9  10
11 12 13 14 15 16 17
18 19 20 21 22 23 24
25 26 27 28
```

MARCH
```
M  T  W  T  F  S  S
            1  2  3
4  5  6  7  8  9  10
11 12 13 14 15 16 17
18 19 20 21 22 23 24
25 26 27 28 29 30 31
```

APRIL
```
M  T  W  T  F  S  S
1  2  3  4  5  6  7
8  9  10 11 12 13 14
15 16 17 18 19 20 21
22 23 24 25 26 27 28
29 30
```

MAY
```
M  T  W  T  F  S  S
      1  2  3  4  5
6  7  8  9  10 11 12
13 14 15 16 17 18 19
20 21 22 23 24 25 26
27 28 29 30 31
```

JUNE
```
M  T  W  T  F  S  S
               1  2
3  4  5  6  7  8  9
10 11 12 13 14 15 16
17 18 19 20 21 22 23
24 25 26 27 28 29 30
```

JULY
```
M  T  W  T  F  S  S
1  2  3  4  5  6  7
8  9  10 11 12 13 14
15 16 17 18 19 20 21
22 23 24 25 26 27 28
29 30 31
```

AUGUST
```
M  T  W  T  F  S  S
         1  2  3  4
5  6  7  8  9  10 11
12 13 14 15 16 17 18
19 20 21 22 23 24 25
26 27 28 29 30 31
```

SEPTEMBER
```
M  T  W  T  F  S  S
                  1
2  3  4  5  6  7  8
9  10 11 12 13 14 15
16 17 18 19 20 21 22
23 24 25 26 27 28 29
30
```

OCTOBER
```
M  T  W  T  F  S  S
1  2  3  4  5  6
7  8  9  10 11 12 13
14 15 16 17 18 19 20
21 22 23 24 25 26 27
28 29 30 31
```

NOVEMBER
```
M  T  W  T  F  S  S
         1  2  3
4  5  6  7  8  9  10
11 12 13 14 15 16 17
18 19 20 21 22 23 24
25 26 27 28 29 30
```

DECEMBER
```
M  T  W  T  F  S  S
                  1
2  3  4  5  6  7  8
9  10 11 12 13 14 15
16 17 18 19 20 21 22
23 24 25 26 27 28 29
30 31
```

GRAHAM STUART THOMAS 1909–2003

2009 saw the centenary of the birth of Graham Stuart Thomas, who was probably the most influential British gardener of the twentieth century (though he would always have denied it; that accolade, he would have said, belonged to Gertrude Jekyll, whom he met in his youth). He was a distinguished nurseryman for thirty years, first with T. Hilling and Co., and then with Sunningdale; the youngest member appointed to the RHS Floral Committee; a garden designer; the author of 17 books and major pamphlets on subjects ranging from rock gardens to ground cover to winter gardening; and mid-century Britain's most eminent authority on roses. And beyond all this, he was for twenty years (1955–74) the Gardens Advisor to the National Trust, and the man who effectively made the restoration of historic gardens part of British cultural life.

But he was also an artist. His father was an artist, and his juvenile notebooks show him quickly developing a knack for perspective drawing and an interest in plants. As first a calligrapher and then as an artist, he helped to design the catalogues published by Hilling and Sunningdale. But it was not until 1962, and the publication of *Shrub roses of today*, that he used his drawings to illustrate one of his proper books.

Thereafter, his paintings and drawings appeared in, among others, his books on roses, his autobiography *Three gardens*, and his magnificent book on *Gardens of the National Trust* (1979), which included pencil sketches of garden scenes as well as portraits of plants.

In 1987, he published *The complete flower paintings and drawings of Graham Stuart Thomas*, bringing together in one volume the works both in pencil and in watercolours that he had hitherto published, as well as many drawings that had never appeared before. All but a few of the drawings reproduced in this volume were included in that work. His 2002 volume *The garden throughout the year* reproduced some additional drawings, most likely new additions to his repertoire. Even so, drawings of *Lathyrus latifolius, Roscoea* and an unnamed iris cultivar have never published before. None of the drawings are dated, a frustration for scholars, though in his publications he did record the dates of a few.

Many of the plants he drew had particular associations with National Trust gardens. Sometimes Graham Thomas introduced the plant into the Trust's gardens; sometimes he took it from a Trust garden and circulated it to the nursery trade.

Graham Thomas's legacy to British gardening was immense and varied, and his drawings are but a minor part of his work. Nonetheless he was a good and careful artist, and his work deserves to be remembered. The drawings reproduced in this volume are interesting not only as portraits of plants, but as records of the associations of the plants with particular British gardens and with the development of 20th-century horticulture.

Brent Elliott

THE ROYAL HORTICULTURAL SOCIETY

DECEMBER & JANUARY

26 *Monday*

Boxing Day (St Stephen's Day)
Holiday, UK, Republic of Ireland,
USA, Australia and New Zealand

27 *Tuesday*

Holiday, UK, Australia and New Zealand

28 *Wednesday*

29 *Thursday*

30 *Friday*

31 *Saturday*

New Year's Eve

1 *Sunday*

New Year's Day
Holiday, Republic of Ireland
First Quarter

A drawing of rose hips. Clockwise from top: *Rosa* 'Nymphenburg', *Rosa moyesii* 'Geranium', 'Penelope', *Rosa filipes* 'Kiftsgate', 'Ormiston Roy', 'Fru Dagmar Hastrup', and 'Penelope'. First published in *Shrub roses of today* (1962).

JANUARY

Holiday, UK, USA, Canada,
Australia and New Zealand

Monday 2

Holiday, Scotland and New Zealand

Tuesday 3

Wednesday 4

Thursday 5

Epiphany

Friday 6

Saturday 7

Sunday 8

Chaenomeles × superba 'Rowallane', a chance seedling found at Rowallane (NT) in 1920, together with
Rhododendron cinnabarinum subsp. *cinnabarinum* 'Conroy' – a cross made by Lord Aberconway at Bodnant (NT)
in 1934, which received an Award of Merit in 1950. First published in *The complete flower paintings* (1987).

JANUARY

9 *Monday*   *Full Moon*

10 *Tuesday*

11 *Wednesday*

12 *Thursday*

13 *Friday*

14 *Saturday*

15 *Sunday*

Hamamelis mollis, a species collected by Charles Maries for the Veitch Nurseries in the 1870s; *Hamamelis ×
intermedia* 'Pallida', a form which was awarded a First Class Certificate in 1958 when exhibited
by the Crown Estates; and *Hamamelis* 'Brevipetala', a cultivar introduced by Hilliers'
nursery in 1950. First published in *Colour in the winter garden* (1967).

JANUARY

Holiday, USA (Martin Luther King's Birthday)
Last Quarter

Monday 16

Tuesday 17

Wednesday 18

Thursday 19

Friday 20

Saturday 21

Sunday 22

A drawing entitled "Winter stems": *Cornus alba, Perovskia atriplicifolia, Cornus alba* 'Elegantissimus', *Cornus alba* 'Sibirica', *Leycesteria formosa*, and *Cornus sericea* 'Flaviramea'. First published in *Colour in the winter garden* (1967).

JANUARY

23 *Monday*   Chinese New Year
                                                                   New Moon

24 *Tuesday*

25 *Wednesday*

26 *Thursday*   Holiday, Australia (Australia Day)

27 *Friday*

28 *Saturday*

29 *Sunday*

Camellia sasanqua 'Crimson King', a cultivar whose history Graham Thomas unsuccessfully tried to trace; and *Viburnum* × *bodnantense* 'Dawn', raised at Bodnant (NT) from a cross between *V. farreri* (formerly known as *V. fragrans*) and *V. grandiflorum*. First published in *Colour in the winter garden* (1967).

JANUARY & FEBRUARY

Monday 30

First Quarter

Tuesday 31

Wednesday 1

Thursday 2

Friday 3

Saturday 4

Sunday 5

Rhododendron lutescens, a species collected by E.H. Wilson for the Veitch
Nurseries in 1904, together with the West Asian species *Cyclamen coum*.
First published in *Colour in the winter garden* (1967).

FEBRUARY

6 *Monday*   Accession of Queen Elizabeth II (Diamond Jubilee)
Holiday, New Zealand (Waitangi Day)

7 *Tuesday*   *Full Moon*

8 *Wednesday*

9 *Thursday*

10 *Friday*

11 *Saturday*

12 *Sunday*

Helleborus 'Bowles's Yellow' and *Helleborus atrorubens*. Bowles gave his plant to the Cambridge Botanic Garden, and Graham Thomas was given a clump during his apprenticeship there in the late 1920s. As it did not come true from seed, he could not determine its ancestry, and called it 'Bowles's Yellow'; unfortunately, it was last listed in the *RHS Plant Finder* in 2000. First published in *Colour in the winter garden (1967)*.

FEBRUARY

Monday 13

Valentine's Day
Last Quarter

Tuesday 14

Wednesday 15

Thursday 16

Friday 17

Saturday 18

Sunday 19

Camellia × williamsii 'Citation', a cultivar which originated at Bodnant (NT)
before 1960. First published in *Gardens of the National Trust* (1979).

FEBRUARY

20 *Monday* — Holiday, USA (Washington's Birthday)

21 *Tuesday* — Shrove Tuesday
New Moon

22 *Wednesday* — Ash Wednesday

23 *Thursday*

24 *Friday*

25 *Saturday*

26 *Sunday*

Helleborus argutifolius (formerly known as *H. corsicus*), a Mediterranean species which has been grown in Britain since the 17th century. Graham Thomas grew it at Wallington (NT), one of his most important garden design commissions for the National Trust. First published in *Colour in the winter garden* (1967).

FEBRUARY & MARCH

Monday 27

Tuesday 28

Wednesday 29

St David's Day
First Quarter

Thursday 1

Friday 2

Saturday 3

Sunday 4

Rhododendron 'Vanessa Pastel', a cross between *Rhododendron griersonianum* and
R. 'Soulbut', raised at Bodnant (NT) in 1930. First published in *The complete flower paintings* (1987).

MARCH

5 *Monday*

6 *Tuesday*

7 *Wednesday*

8 *Thursday*   *Full Moon*

9 *Friday*

10 *Saturday*

11 *Sunday*

Primula reidii var. *williamsii:* a form collected by two expeditions to the Himalayas, led by Oleg Polunin and Adam Stainton respectively, in 1952 and 1954, and exhibited to acclaim in 1954. First published in *The complete flower paintings* (1987).

Commonwealth Day

Monday 12

Tuesday 13

Wednesday 14

Last Quarter

Thursday 15

Friday 16

St Patrick's Day
Holiday, Republic of Ireland

Saturday 17

Mother's Day, UK

Sunday 18

An ornamental group of *Bergenia purpurascens, Elaeagnus pungens* 'Dicksonii', *Hedera algeriensis* 'Gloire de Marengo', *Iris foetidissima* 'Variegata', *Arum italicum* subsp. *italicum* 'Marmoratum', and *Mahonia* 'Heterophylla' (of unknown, probably hybrid, origin, found by the Wisley botanist N.K. Gould near Tunbridge Wells in 1951). First published in *The garden throughout the year* (2002).

MARCH

---

19 *Monday*

Holiday, Northern Ireland
(St Patrick's Day)

---

20 *Tuesday*

Vernal Equinox (Spring begins)

---

21 *Wednesday*

---

22 *Thursday*

New Moon

---

23 *Friday*

---

24 *Saturday*

---

25 *Sunday*

British Summer Time begins

Rhododendron × laerdal, a hybrid between *R. dalhousieae* and *R. johnstoneanum* raised at Trengwainton (NT) in the 1930s, but not widely known until the 1960s. The other plant depicted is *Kennedia rubicunda,* an Australian plant also grown at Trengwainton. First published in *Gardens of the National Trust* (1979).

MARCH & APRIL

Monday 26

Tuesday 27

Wednesday 28

Thursday 29

First Quarter

Friday 30

Saturday 31

Palm Sunday

Sunday 1

Two flowering shrubs associated with Nymans (NT): *Magnolia × loebneri* 'Leonard Messel', which began life as a seedling from *Magnolia stellata* 'Rosea', and *Forsythia suspensa* 'Nymans'. First published in *Gardens of the National Trust* (1979).

APRIL

2 *Monday*

3 *Tuesday*

4 *Wednesday*

5 *Thursday*

Maundy Thursday

6 *Friday*

Good Friday
Holiday, UK, Canada, Australia and New Zealand
Full Moon

7 *Saturday*

Holiday, Australia (Easter Saturday)
First Day of Passover (Pesach)

8 *Sunday*

Easter Sunday

Fritillaria michailovskyi, a Turkish species, collected by the Kew-sponsored Flora of Turkey expedition in 1969. Kew later exhibited it at the RHS in 1983 and it received an Award of Merit. Drawn in 1986, and published in *The complete flower paintings* (1987).

APRIL

Easter Monday
Holiday, UK (exc. Scotland), Republic of Ireland,
Australia and New Zealand

Monday 9

Tuesday 10

Wednesday 11

Thursday 12

Last Quarter

Friday 13

Saturday 14

Sunday 15

Primula 'Devon Cream', a cultivar found at the Garden House, Buckland Monachorum, Devon, before the Second World War, and *Viola* 'Huntercombe Purple', an old-fashioned cultivar bred by Eleanor Vere Boyle, who wrote under the name E.V.B., and whose garden at Huntercombe, Buckinghamshire, was influential in the late 19th century. First published in *The complete flower paintings* (1987).

16 *Monday*

17 *Tuesday*

18 *Wednesday*

19 *Thursday*

20 *Friday*

21 *Saturday*

Birthday of Queen Elizabeth II
New Moon

22 *Sunday*

Two June-flowering irises: *Iris graminea* and *Iris kerneriana*.
First published in Graham Stuart Thomas' *Three gardens* (1983).

APRIL

St George's Day

Monday 23

Tuesday 24

Holiday, Australia and New Zealand
(Anzac Day)

Wednesday 25

Thursday 26

Friday 27

Saturday 28

First Quarter

Sunday 29

Two traditional bulbous plants: *Chionodoxa luciliae*, which was introduced in 1877 by the tile manufacturer and plant collector George Maw at his house Benthall Hall, Shropshire (now NT). With it is *Narcissus 'Eystettensis'*, a 17th-century cultivar. The *chionodoxa* part of the drawing was reproduced in *Gardens of the National Trust* (1979).

30 *Monday*

1 *Tuesday*

2 *Wednesday*

3 *Thursday*

4 *Friday*

5 *Saturday*

6 *Sunday*

Full Moon

Trillium catesbyi (formerly known under the obsolete spelling *catesbaei)*, native to the southeast United States and named for the 18th-century naturalist Mark Catesby, was introduced in the 1820s but little grown in British gardens until after the Second World War. First published in *The complete flower paintings* (1987).

MAY

Early Spring Bank Holiday, UK and Republic of Ireland

Monday 7

Tuesday 8

Wednesday 9

Thursday 10

Friday 11

Last Quarter

Saturday 12

Mother's Day, USA, Canada,
Australia and New Zealand

Sunday 13

Camassia leichtlinii subsp. *suksdorfii* 'Lady Eve Price', a cultivar raised by Sir Henry Price at his garden,
Wakehurst Place (later NT), which was given an Award of Merit in 1963. First published in *The garden
throughout the year* (2002).

MAY

14 *Monday*

15 *Tuesday*

16 *Wednesday*

17 *Thursday*   Ascension Day

18 *Friday*

19 *Saturday*

20 *Sunday*   *New Moon*

Magnolia × thompsoniana, a 19th-century hybrid between *M. tripetala* and *M. virginiana*.
Graham Thomas recommended it to Trengwainton (NT), where Edward Bolitho was already growing all
the magnolias he could. First published in Graham Stuart Thomas' *Three gardens* (1983).

MAY

Holiday, Canada (Victoria Day)

Monday 21

Tuesday 22

Wednesday 23

Thursday 24

Friday 25

Saturday 26

Whit Sunday (Pentecost)
Feast of Weeks (Shavuot)

Sunday 27

Rosa 'Nymphenburg' was bred by the celebrated German rose grower Wilhelm Kordes, and launched in 1954. First published in *Shrub roses of today* (1962).

MAY & JUNE

28 *Monday*

First Quarter
Holiday, USA (Memorial Day)

29 *Tuesday*

30 *Wednesday*

31 *Thursday*

1 *Friday*

2 *Saturday*

Coronation Day

3 *Sunday*

Trinity Sunday

Origanum 'Kent Beauty' and its parents, *Origanum scabrum* and *Origanum rotundifolium*.
It was bred by Elizabeth Strangman of the Washfield Nursery in the 1970s.
First published in *The complete flower paintings* (1987).

JUNE

Spring Bank Holiday, UK
Holiday, Republic of Ireland
Holiday, New Zealand (The Queen's Birthday)
Full Moon

Monday 4

Holiday, UK (The Queen's Diamond Jubilee)

Tuesday 5

Wednesday 6

Corpus Christi

Thursday 7

Friday 8

The Queen's Official Birthday (subject to confirmation)

Saturday 9

Sunday 10

Three cultivars associated with Hidcote (NT): *Hypericum* 'Hidcote', which by mid-century had become the most popular *hypericum* variety (and which Lawrence Johnston claimed to have collected in China); *Penstemon* 'Hidcote'; and *Fuchsia* 'Hidcote'. First published in *The complete flower paintings* (1987).

JUNE

11 *Monday*

Holiday, Australia (The Queen's Birthday),
subject to confirmation
Last Quarter

12 *Tuesday*

13 *Wednesday*

14 *Thursday*

15 *Friday*

16 *Saturday*

17 *Sunday*

Father's Day, UK, Canada and USA

Two roses bred by the Orléans firm of Barbier & Cie: 'Auguste Gervais' (1918) and
'Alexandre Girault' (1909), both more popular today on the continent of Europe than
in Britain. First published in *Climbing roses old and new* (1965).

JUNE

Monday 18

New Moon

Tuesday 19

Summer Solstice (Summer begins)

Wednesday 20

Thursday 21

Friday 22

Saturday 23

Sunday 24

Meconopsis 'Slieve Donard' (infertile blue group): a hybrid between *Meconopsis grandis* and *M. betonicifolia*, raised at Mount Stewart (NT), where it was called 'Prain's Variety', and given to the Slieve Donard nursery in the 1930s. First published in *Gardens of the National Trust* (1979).

JUNE & JULY

25 *Monday*

26 *Tuesday*

27 *Wednesday*   *First Quarter*

28 *Thursday*

29 *Friday*

30 *Saturday*

1 *Sunday*   Canada Day

Two plants of Himalayan origin: *Hypericum bellum*, in the undulate-leaved form introduced by Ludlow and Sherriff in 1947, and below, *Geranium wallichianum* 'Buxton's Variety', which Thomas described as "a pearl beyond price". First published in Graham Stuart Thomas' *Three gardens* (1983).

JULY

Holiday, Canada (Canada Day)

Monday 2

Full Moon

Tuesday 3

Holiday, USA (Independence Day)

Wednesday 4

Thursday 5

Friday 6

Saturday 7

Sunday 8

Cypripedium reginae, an American species of slipper orchid: a drawing made in 1930, when Thomas, aged 20, was learning how to grow native British orchids. First published in *The complete flower paintings* (1987).

JULY

9 *Monday*

10 *Tuesday*

11 *Wednesday*   *Last Quarter*

12 *Thursday*   Holiday, Northern Ireland (Battle of the Boyne)

13 *Friday*

14 *Saturday*

15 *Sunday*   St Swithin's Day

Rosa 'Golden Wings', a cultivar raised in 1958 by the American amateur Roy Shepherd, whose *History of the rose* (1954) was the classic in the field before Graham Thomas began publishing. Also shown is *Rosa* 'Erfurt', introduced by Wilhelm Kordes in 1931. First published in *Shrub roses of today* (1962).

C.S.Thomas
1930

JULY

Monday 16

Tuesday 17

Wednesday 18

New Moon

Thursday 19

First day of Ramadân (subject to sighting of the moon)

Friday 20

Saturday 21

Sunday 22

An unidentified iris cultivar; not previously published.

JULY

---

23 *Monday*

---

24 *Tuesday*

---

25 *Wednesday*

---

26 *Thursday*   *First Quarter*

---

27 *Friday*

---

28 *Saturday*

---

29 *Sunday*

Four old clove carnations. From the top: 'Lord Chatham', an 18th-century cultivar also known as 'Raby Castle';
an unnamed striped sport; a crimson clove; and a cultivar unnamed when the drawing was first published
in G. S. Thomas' *Three gardens* (1983), but sometimes called 'Starcross' after the village where it was found.

JULY & AUGUST

Monday 30

Tuesday 31

Wednesday 1

Full Moon   *Thursday* 2

Friday 3

Saturday 4

Sunday 5

Hypericum 'Rowallane', a hybrid between *H. leschenaultii* and *H. hookerianum* 'Rogersii'; the original seedling was found growing at Rowallane (NT) and introduced into cultivation by the garden's owner, Hugh Armytage Moore, receiving an Award of Merit in 1943. First published in *Gardens of the National Trust* (1979).

AUGUST

6 *Monday*

Summer Bank Holiday, Scotland
Holiday, Republic of Ireland

7 *Tuesday*

8 *Wednesday*

9 *Thursday*

Last Quarter

10 *Friday*

11 *Saturday*

12 *Sunday*

Lathyrus nervosus, or Lord Anson's blue pea. This was found in Patagonia on Lord Anson's expedition around the world (1704–44), and introduced by him through his brother's estate at Shugborough. When the National Trust acquired Shugborough in 1966, Graham Thomas acquired seeds of the pea to ensure it was once again planted there. First published in *Gardens of the National Trust* (1979).

AUGUST

Monday 13

Tuesday 14

Wednesday 15

Thursday 16

New Moon

Friday 17

Saturday 18

Eid-al-Fitr (end of Ramadân)

Sunday 19

Rosa multibracteata, a Chinese species introduced by E.H. Wilson in 1910, with *Rosa* 'Cerise Bouquet', a cultivar launched by Wilhelm Kordes in 1958. First published in *Shrub roses of today* (1962).

AUGUST

20 *Monday*

21 *Tuesday*

22 *Wednesday*

23 *Thursday*

24 *Friday*   *First Quarter*

25 *Saturday*

26 *Sunday*

*Four modern cultivars of Hibiscus syriacus: 'Blue Bird', 'Woodbridge', 'Dorothy Crane',
and 'Hamabo'. First published in Graham Stuart Thomas' Three gardens (1983).*

AUGUST & SEPTEMBER

Summer Bank Holiday UK (exc. Scotland)

Monday 27

Tuesday 28

Wednesday 29

Thursday 30

Full Moon

Friday 31

Saturday 1

Sunday 2

Three *Crocosmia* cultivars, commonly called montbretias: from the top, 'Star of the East', 'Vesuvius', and 'Queen of Spain'. The first and third received awards from the RHS before the First World War. First published in Graham Stuart Thomas' *Three gardens* (1983).

SEPTEMBER

3 *Monday*

Holiday, USA (Labor Day)
Holiday, Canada (Labour Day)

4 *Tuesday*

5 *Wednesday*

6 *Thursday*

7 *Friday*

8 *Saturday*

Last Quarter

9 *Sunday*

A drawing of species of *Roscoea*, an Asiatic genus of plants
related to the gingers. Not previously published.

SEPTEMBER

Monday 10

Tuesday 11

Wednesday 12

Thursday 13

Friday 14

Saturday 15

New Moon

Sunday 16

Campanula latiloba and some of its cultivars: *Campanula latiloba* 'Hidcote Amethyst', a sport found at Hidcote (NT) in the 1960s; *Campanula latiloba,* the species; *Campanula latiloba* 'Highcliffe Variety', and *Campanula latiloba* 'Alba'. First published in *Gardens of the National Trust* (1979).

SEPTEMBER

17 *Monday*   Jewish New Year (Rosh Hashanah)

18 *Tuesday*

19 *Wednesday*

20 *Thursday*

21 *Friday*

22 *Saturday*   Autumnal Equinox (Autumn begins)
First Quarter

23 *Sunday*

Rosa 'Madame de Sancy de Parabère', introduced in 1874 by the Bonnet nursery in Nancy, and 'Amadis',
a Boursault rose introduced by Laffay in 1829. First published in *Climbing roses old and new* (1965).

SEPTEMBER

Monday 24

Tuesday 25

Day of Atonement (Yom Kippur)

Wednesday 26

Thursday 27

Friday 28

Michaelmas Day

Saturday 29

Full Moon

Sunday 30

Forms of the American species *Phlox nana:* 'Arroyo' (first described under the obsolete specific name of *Phlox mesoleuca)* and 'Mary Maslin'. Drawn in 1986, and published in *The complete flower paintings* (1987).

OCTOBER

1 *Monday*

Holiday, Australia (Labour Day), subject to confirmation
First Day of Tabernacles (Succoth)

2 *Tuesday*

3 *Wednesday*

4 *Thursday*

5 *Friday*

6 *Saturday*

7 *Sunday*

Clematis viticella 'Purpurea Plena Elegans' *Clematis* 'Etoile Rose'. Both cultivars were introduced into commerce by Graham Thomas through Sunningdale Nursery, the latter from Mark Fenwick's garden at Abbotswood, Gloucestershire. What he initially called *Clematis* 'Elegans Plena' was also grown by Fenwick, but Thomas reported that he had in fact used a specimen at Charlecote (NT) to propagate from. First published in Graham Stuart Thomas' *Three gardens* (1983).

Holiday, USA (Columbus Day)
Holiday, Canada (Thanksgiving)
Last Quarter

Two plants associated with gardens now owned by the National Trust. *Eucryphia × nymansensis*, a cross between *E. glutinosa* and *E. cordifolia*, was raised at Nymans in 1914. *Fuchsia* 'Mount Stewart' was raised at Mount Stewart in Northern Ireland, and introduced into commerce in the 1980s – after this drawing was published in *Gardens of the National Trust* (1979).

OCTOBER

15 *Monday*   *New Moon*

16 *Tuesday*

17 *Wednesday*

18 *Thursday*

19 *Friday*

20 *Saturday*

21 *Sunday*

The montbretias (*Crocosmia* × *crocosmiiflora* hybrids) were first bred by Victor Lemoine of Nancy
in the 1880s; 'Solfaterre', right, is one of his early crosses. The others are earlham montbretias,
bred in Norfolk in the early 20th century: 'Nimbus', top, and 'Mrs George Howard', lower left.
First published in *The complete flower paintings* (1987).

OCTOBER

Holiday, New Zealand (Labour Day)
First Quarter

Monday 22

Tuesday 23

United Nations Day

Wednesday 24

Thursday 25

Friday 26

Saturday 27

British Summer Time ends

Sunday 28

Two climbing varieties of well-known early 20th-century roses, which became more popular than their original bush forms: 'Climbing Mrs Herbert Stevens' (Pernet-Ducher, 1922), and 'Climbing Lady Hillingdon' (J.S. Hicks of Texas, 1917). First published in *Climbing roses old and new* (1965).

OCTOBER & NOVEMBER

29 *Monday*

Holiday, Republic of Ireland
Full Moon

30 *Tuesday*

31 *Wednesday*

Hallowe'en

1 *Thursday*

All Saints' Day

2 *Friday*

3 *Saturday*

4 *Sunday*

Penstemon 'Rubicundus', a cultivar first raised at Lyme Park (NT)
in 1906. First published in *Gardens of the National Trust* (1979).

NOVEMBER

Guy Fawkes

Monday 5

Tuesday 6

Last Quarter

Wednesday 7

Thursday 8

Friday 9

Saturday 10

Remembrance Sunday, UK

Sunday 11

Two cultivars of *Pieris* associated with National Trust gardens. *Pieris formosa* var. *forrestii* 'Wakehurst', a cultivar of the variety commonly called "Forrest's pieris", together with *Pieris japonica* 'Rowallane', a once popular cultivar last listed as commercially available in 2000. First published in *Gardens of the National Trust* (1979).

NOVEMBER

12 *Monday*

Holiday, USA (Veterans Day)
Holiday, Canada (Remembrance Day)

13 *Tuesday*

New Moon

14 *Wednesday*

15 *Thursday*

Islamic New Year begins (subject to sighting of the moon)

16 *Friday*

17 *Saturday*

18 *Sunday*

This drawing shows five stages in the development of *Rosa × odorata* 'Mutabilis', a rose of uncertain origin and date, introduced into commerce by the Swiss nurseryman Henri Correvon in 1933. Also shown is an English cultivar, 'Buff Beauty', bred by J.A. Bentall of Havering in 1939, and today the most widely grown of Hybrid Musk roses. First published in *Shrub roses of today* (1962).

NOVEMBER

Monday 19

First Quarter

Tuesday 20

Wednesday 21

Holiday, USA (Thanksgiving Day)

Thursday 22

Friday 23

Saturday 24

Sunday 25

Two flowers associated with National Trust gardens: *Crocosmia masoniorum* 'Rowallane Yellow', a sport discovered at Rowallane in the early 1970s, and *Dianthus* 'Hidcote', of uncertain date but grown at Hidcote before 1950. First published in *Gardens of the National Trust* (1979).

NOVEMBER & DECEMBER

26 *Monday*

27 *Tuesday*

28 *Wednesday* — *Full Moon*

29 *Thursday*

30 *Friday* — St Andrew's Day

1 *Saturday*

2 *Sunday* — First Sunday in Advent

Iris foetidissima var. *citrina*, a naturally occurring variety that can be found in southwest England, and *Crataegus × lavalleei* 'Carrierei', a hybrid raised around 1870 at the Jardin des Plantes in Paris. First published in *Colour in the winter garden* (1967).

DECEMBER

Monday 3

Tuesday 4

Wednesday 5

'*Last Quarter*

Thursday 6

Friday 7

Saturday 8

Hannukah begins

Sunday 9

'Dream Girl', a *Rosa wichuraiana* hybrid, was bred by the New Jersey rosarian Martin Jacobus in 1944; popular as a pillar rose in the mid-20th century, it was last listed as commercially available in 2008. First published in *Climbing roses old and new* (1965).

DECEMBER

10 *Monday*

11 *Tuesday*

12 *Wednesday*

13 *Thursday*   *New Moon*

14 *Friday*

15 *Saturday*

16 *Sunday*

Lathyrus latifolius, the everlasting pea, a native species of Europe.
Not previously published.

DECEMBER

Monday 17

Tuesday 18

Wednesday 19

First Quarter   *Thursday* 20

Winter Solstice (Winter begins)   *Friday* 21

Saturday 22

Sunday 23

Two Hybrid Musk roses bred by the celebrated Romford rosarian Joseph Pemberton: 'Vanity' (1920),
last listed in the RHS *Plant Finder* in 2007, and 'Pax' (1918). First published in *Shrub roses of today* (1962).

DECEMBER

24 *Monday*   Christmas Eve

25 *Tuesday*

Christmas Day
Holiday, UK, Republic of Ireland, USA, Canada,
Australia and New Zealand

26 *Wednesday*

Boxing Day (St Stephen's Day)
Holiday, UK, Republic of Ireland,
Australia and New Zealand

27 *Thursday*

28 *Friday*   *Full Moon*

29 *Saturday*

30 *Sunday*

Rosa 'Lawrence Johnston' was originally bred by Pernet-Ducher in the 1920s, and introduced to
Hidcote (NT) by Johnston; in 1950, Graham Thomas introduced it through Hilling's as 'Hidcote Yellow',
but renamed it in order to avoid confusion with 'Hidcote Gold'. Also *Rosa* 'Cupid', a Hybrid Tea
introduced by Cants of Colchester in 1915. First published in *Climbing roses old and new* (1965).

DECEMBER & JANUARY

31 *Monday* New Year's Eve

1 *Tuesday* New Year's Day
Holiday, UK, Republic of Ireland, USA, Canada,
Australia and New Zealand

2 *Wednesday* Holiday, Scotland and New Zealand

3 *Thursday*

4 *Friday*

5 *Saturday* *Last Quarter*

6 *Sunday* Epiphany